# HORRID HENRY'S JUMBO JOKE BOOK

**Francesca Simon** spent her childhood in California, and then went to Yale and Oxford Universities to study medieval history and literature. She now lives in London with her family. She has written over fifty books and won the Children's Book Of The Year in 2008 at the Galaxy British Book Awards for *Horrid Henry And The Abominable Snowman*.

**Tony Ross** is one of Britain's best known illustrators, with many picture books to his name. He has also produced the line drawings for many fiction titles, for authors such as David Walliams, Jeanne Willis, Enid Blyton, Astrid Lindgren, and many more. He lives in Wales.

## Also by Fancesca Simon

*Don't Cook Cinderella*
*Helping Hercules*

and for younger readers

*Don't Be Horrid, Henry!*
*The Parent Swap Shop*
*Spider School*
*The Topsy-Turvies*

For a complete list of **Horrid Henry** titles visit
www.horridhenry.co.uk
or
www.orionchildrensbooks.co.uk

# HORRID HENRY'S JUMBO JOKE BOOK

## Francesca Simon

### Illustrated by Tony Ross

Orion
Children's Books

ORION CHILDREN'S BOOKS

This collection first published in Great Britain in 2015 by Orion Children's Books
This edition published in 2016 by Hodder and Stoughton

1 3 5 7 9 10 8 6 4 2

Text copyright © Francesca Simon
Illustrations copyright © Tony Ross

The moral rights of the author and illustrator have been asserted.

A CIP catalogue record for this book
is available from the British Library.

ISBN 978 1 4440 1571 3

Printed and bound in Great Britain
by Clays Ltd, St Ives plc

The paper and board used in this book are
made from wood from responsible sources.

MIX
Paper from
responsible sources
FSC® C104740

Orion Children's Books
An imprint of
Hachette Children's Group
Part of Hodder and Stoughton
Carmelite House
50 Victoria Embankment
London EC4Y 0DZ

An Hachette UK Company
www.hachette.co.uk

www.hachettechildrens.co.uk

# CONTENTS

# CONTENTS

# HORRID HENRY'S
# HILARIOUSLY
# HORRID
# JOKE BOOK

# CONTENTS

# HORRID HENRY'S HILARIOUSLY HORRID JOKE BOOK

Phew. I'm exhausted. Instead of spending Christmas lounging on the comfy black chair eating Belcher Squelchers and watching Knight Fight, I've been writing my best joke book yet. I've got 365 extra special, super-duper fantastically funny jokes, one for every single day of the year.

Anyway, Happy New Year everyone. Except of course, Peter. And Margaret. And Steve. And Bill. And Rebecca. Nasty New Year to all my evil enemies. But a great one to Purple Hand Gang members everywhere!

# HAPPY NEW YEAR

*Knock, knock!*
Who's there?
*Happy.*
Happy who?
*Happy New Year!*

*What do
vampires sing
on New Year's Eve?*
Old Fang Syne.

*What's a cow's favourite
day of the year?*
MOO Year's Day!

*And what's a cat's favourite day?*
MEW Year's Day!

**GRUMPY NEXT-DOOR NEIGHBOUR:**
Didn't you hear me banging on your
wall last night?
**HAPPY NEXT-DOOR NEIGHBOUR:**
Oh, don't worry about it. We had a New
Year's Eve party and made lots of noise too.

*Where does Tarzan
buy his clothes?*
At a jungle sale.

*How many months
have twenty-eight days?*
All of them.

*How many seconds are there in a year?*
Twelve. The 2nd of January, the 2nd
of February, the 2nd of March…

# JOLLY JOKES
# TO START
# THE YEAR

What occurs once in a minute, twice
in a moment, but never in an hour?
The letter 'm'.

What do you take the top
off to put the bottom on?
A toilet seat.

What do you call a dinosaur
with only one eye?
A Do-you-think-he-saw-us.

What do you call a dinosaur
that changes its mind?
A Now-I'm-not-so-sure-us.

*How do you know when there's
an elephant under your bed?*
Your nose touches the ceiling.

*Why is getting up at six o'clock in
the morning like a pig's tail?*
It's twirly!

*Why was the mermaid thrown out of the choir?*
She couldn't carry a tuna.

*What do you get when you cross
a knight with a mosquito?*
A bite in shining armour.

*Why is the sky so high?*
So that birds won't bump their heads.

*What's the difference between
a unicorn and a lettuce?*
One's a funny beast and
the other's a bunny feast.

*How do you fix a tuba?*
With a tuba glue.

*What did the Sheriff
of Nottingham say
when Robin Hood
fired at him and
missed?*

That was an-arrow
escape.

# FEBRUARY FUN

**Yay! February's my birthday.**
**Line up, line up, lots of presents**
**needed!**

*Why did Lazy Linda go to bed early?*
Because she was feeling Febru-weary.

*What did the boy squirrel say to the girl squirrel*
*on Valentine's Day?*
I'm nuts about you!

*What did the girl squirrel say
to the boy squirrel?*
You're nuts so bad yourself!

*What did the ram say to his girlfriend
on Valentine's Day?*
I love ewe.

*What did the caveman give his girlfriend on
Valentine's Day?*
Ugs and kisses.

*Why did the acrobats get married?*
They were head over heels in love.

What do you call a very small Valentine?
A Valentiny!

Roses are red, violets are blue,
Most poems rhyme,
But this one doesn't.
Tee hee!

What's green and only comes out
on February 29th?
A leapfrog.

# BIRTHDAY BELLY-LAUGHS

*What's a camel's favourite party game?*
Musical Humps.

*What's a cow's favourite party game?*
Moosical Chairs.

*What do you say to a cow on its birthday?*
Happy birthday to moo.

**That one's for you, Maggie Moo Moo.**

*Don't call me that!*

**Call you what, Moo Moo?**

*What do you say to a cat on its birthday?*
Happy birthday to mew.

*What do you say to a parrot
on its birthday?*
Happy birdy to you.

*What do you get every birthday?*
A year older.

**TOUGH TOBY:** Henry, when is
your birthday?
**HORRID HENRY:** Every year!

*What's the best birthday present in the world?*
A broken drum, you can't beat it!

# KNOCK, KNOCK!
# SPRING'S HERE

**(About time, too.)**

*Knock, knock!*
Who's there?
*Woo.*
Woo, who?
*Calm down, it's just a joke.*

    *Knock, knock!*
    Who's there?
    *A little old man.*
    A little old man who?
    *A little old man who can't reach the doorbell.*

*Knock, knock!*
Who's there?
*Let us.*
Let us who?
*Let us in and you'll soon find out.*

*Knock, knock!*
Who's there?
*Dishes.*
Dishes who?
*Dishes me.*
Who ish you?

*Knock, knock!*
Who's there?
*Gorilla.*
Gorilla who?
*Gorilla me some cheese on toast, I'm hungry.*

*Knock, knock!*
Who's there?
*Tank!*
Tank who?
*You're welcome!*

# SPRING

Spring. Birds tweeting.
Trees budding.
Butterflies flapping.
Yeah, who cares, right?
Spring means April Fools' Day!
And great jokes to annoy little
brothers and sisters!
And loads and loads and loads
of chocolate for Easter!

# SPRING SIDESPLITTERS

*Knock, knock!*
Who's there?
*Cook.*
Cook who?
*That's the first cuckoo I've heard this year.*

*What's green and jumps around the garden?*
A spring onion.

*Why did the hen leap over the road?*
She was a spring chicken.

*Can February March?*
No, but April May!

*What colour is the wind?*
Blew.

*Why is everyone tired on April 1st?*
Because they've just finished a 31-day March.

*When's the best time to go
on a trampoline?*
Spring!

**How does Peter frog feel
when he has a broken leg?**
*Very unhoppy.*

Mum! Henry
called me
a frog!

*How do you make a butterfly?*
Flick it out of the dish with a butter
knife.

*What do you call the snail
that crossed the road?*
Lucky.

*What did the mother worm
say to the baby worm?*
Where in earth have
you been?

*What's green and sits in the corner?*
A naughty frog.

**A naughty frog-face named Peter
- tee hee!**

Mum!

# RAINY RIBTICKLERS

*Who designed the first
rain jacket?*
Anna Rack.

*What goes up when the
rain comes down?*
An umbrella.

*What do Jelly Babies wear in the rain?*
Gum boots.

*What's the difference between a wet day and a lion with toothache?*
One's pouring with rain; the other's roaring with pain.

*When should a mouse carry an umbrella?*
When it's raining cats and dogs.

*What do owls sing when it's raining?*
Too wet to woo.

# PONGY PETS

*Why did the man buy all the birds*
*at the pet shop?*
They were going
cheep.

**MUM:** Have you given the goldfish
their fresh water?
**LAZY LINDA:** No, they haven't
drunk the water I gave them last
week yet.

Moody Margaret saw Horrid Henry
with a newt on his shoulder.
"What do you call him?" asked
Moody Margaret.
"Tiny," said Horrid Henry.
"Why do you call him Tiny?"
"Because he's my newt!"

**PATIENT:** Doctor! Doctor!
I think I need glasses.
**DOCTOR:** I think you're right.
This is a pet shop!

*What do you call a really happy rodent?*
A grinny pig.

*What did the dog say when he sat on the
sandpaper?*
Rough, rough.

*Where do you find a birthday present for a cat?*
In a cat-alogue.

**NEW NICK:** I play scrabble
with my dog every night.
**BRAINY BRIAN:**
He must be clever.
**NEW NICK:**
I don't know about
that. I usually beat him.

*When is it bad to have a black cat
following you?*
When you're a mouse.

*What do you say to a miserable budgie?*
Chirrup.

# APRIL FOOLS' DAY FUN

*On April Fools' Day, what goes "He he, bonk"?*
Horrid Henry laughing his head off.

*Do you know what happens on April 1st?*
Yes, I'm fooly aware of it!

*What would you get if you crossed April 1st with Halloween?*
April Ghouls' Day.

**HORRID HENRY:** If a red house is made of red bricks, and a blue house is made of blue bricks, what's a green house made of?

**PERFECT PETER:** Green bricks, of course.

**HORRID HENRY:** Fooled you! It's made of GLASS!

**Peter is a frog, Peter is a frog!**

Muuuuuum! Henry's being horrid.

**Dont be horrid, Henry!**

**RUDE RALPH:** What's green and purple, with googly eyes and big sharp teeth?

**HORRID HENRY:** I don't know. Why?

**RUDE RALPH:** Because one's just climbing up your leg!

*Knock, knock!*
Who's there?
*Twitter.*
Twitter who?
*Ha ha! You sound just like an owl!*

*Will you remember me tomorrow?*
Yes.
*Will you remember me next week?*
Yes.
*Will you remember me next month?*
Yes.
*Will you remember me next year?*
Yes.
*Knock, knock!*
Who's there?
*April Fools! You've forgotten me already!*

**RUDE RALPH:** I'm so thirsty mymy
tongue's hanging out.
**MOODY MARGARET:** Is that your
tongue? It looks like a horrible spotted tie.

**Peter, what's
frozen water?**

It's ice, Henry.

**What's frozen
cream?**

That's easy, ice-cream.

**What about frozen tea?**

Iced tea.

**And frozen ink?**

Iced ink.

**Ha ha, Peter! April Fools –
you'd better have a bath then!**

Mum! Henry said I stink!

**Did not!**

Did too!

**MUM:** Why have you been sent home from school early?

**HORRID HENRY:** I set fire to something in cookery class.

**MUM:** Oh dear! What was it?

**HORRID HENRY:** The school!
………Ha ha! April Fools!

**HORRID HENRY:** Why have you got a sausage behind your ear?

**MISS BATTLE-AXE:** Oh no, I must have eaten my pencil for lunch!

**HORRID HENRY:** April Fools!

*What do you have in April that you don't have in any other month?*
The letter 'i'!

*How do you make Beefy Bert laugh
on April Fools' Day?*
Tell him a joke on the 31st March.

**HORRID HENRY:** What sort
of candle burns longer?
**MUM:** Mm… I'll have to think
carefully about that one.
**HORRID HENRY:** April Fools!
They all burn SHORTER!

**HORRID HENRY:**
Dad, have you heard
the latest newsflash?
A 4-foot man and a
9-foot woman have
just escaped from
prison. The police are
looking HIGH and
LOW for them – tee
hee!

# FUNNY FARMYARDS

*What do you call a donkey with
only three legs?*
A wonkey.

*What do you call a cow eating grass?*
A lawn moo-er.

*What do you call a pony with a sore throat?*
A little horse.

*What do you get when you cross
a chicken with a thief?*
A peck-pocket.

*Did you know it takes three sheep
to make a sweater?*
I didn't even know they could knit!

*What kind of tie does a pig wear?*
A pig-sty.

**1ST COW:** Have you heard about
this mad cow disease?
**2ND COW:** Don't ask me, I'm a
buttercup!

*What goes moo, baa, oink, woof, quack?*
A cow that can speak five languages.

# BEASTLY LITTLE BROTHER AND STINKY LITTLE SISTER JOKES

**MUM:** I'm going to the doctor's. I don't like the look of your little brother.
**HORRID HENRY:** I'll come with you. I don't like the look of him either.

*Does your little brother keep himself clean?*
Oh yes. He takes a bath every month whether he needs one or not.

**LISPY LILY:** Shall I put the telly on?
**NEW NICK:** It might look better than that dress you're wearing.

**HORRID HENRY:** Why are you sitting in the rabbit's cage?

**PERFECT PETER:** Because I want to be the teacher's pet.

*How many little brothers and sisters does it take to do the washing-up after lunch?*

Three – one to wash, one to dry and one to pick up the pieces.

**DAD:** What's on the telly tonight?
**PERFECT PETER:** Same as always, Dad, a vase of flowers and a picture of Grandma.

*What happens when your little sister falls down on the ice?*
She gets thaw.

*How many little brothers and sisters does it take to change a light bulb?*
Ten! One to change the light bulb and nine to stand on each other's shoulders!

# EASTER WISECRACKS

*Why did the boiled egg win the race?*
It couldn't be beaten.

*Why shouldn't you tell
an Easter egg a joke?*
It might crack up.

*What did one Easter egg
say to the other?*
Got any good yolks.

*How do rabbits stay fit?*
EGG-xercise and HARE-robics!

*What do you call a rabbit that
tells good jokes?*
A funny bunny!

*Why do we paint eggs at Easter?*
Because it's easier than trying to
wallpaper them.

*Why did the egg go into the jungle?*
Because it was an EGG-splorer.

*What do you call a chick that
wears a shellsuit?*
An egg!

# KNOCK, KNOCK!
# LET IN THE
# SUMMER

**Race you to the
Frosty-Freeze
ice cream factory!**

*Knock, knock!*
Who's there?
*Luck.*
Luck who?
*Luck through the keyhole and you'll find out.*

*Knock, knock!*
Who's there?
*Wooden shoe.*
Wooden shoe who?
*Wooden shoe like to know?*

*Knock, knock!*
Who's there?
*Atch.*
Atch who?
*Bless you!*

*Knock, knock!*
Who's there?
*Ya.*
Ya who?
*I didn't know you were a cowboy!*

*Knock, knock!*
Who's there?
*Felix.*
Felix who?
*Felix my ice-cream, I'll lick his.*

*Knock, knock!*
Who's there?
*Cash.*
Cash who?
*I knew you were nuts.*

# SUMMER

Summer! At last! Throw away those school books! No more carrot nose Miss Battle-Axe! No more tests! No more fractions! Now it's just fun fun fun. And loads of ice cream and lying in the sun blasting out The Killer Boy Rats and playing video games and - go away, Peter. I'm busy.

Henry, won't you play with me?

NO!

# SPORTING GAGS

**SUSAN:** Mum, Miss Battle-Axe says I need new trainers for gym.
**MUM:** Well, tell her Jim will have to buy his own trainers.

*Why doesn't the centipede get picked for the football team?*
It takes him hours to get his boots on.

Horrid Henry missed a shot at goal, and the other team won. "I could kick myself," he moaned. "Don't bother," said Moody Margaret, "you'd miss!"

**MOODY MARGARET:** I'm sorry I'm late for school, Miss, but I was dreaming about football.

**MISS BATTLE-AXE:** Why does dreaming about football make you late for school?

**MOODY MARGARET:** They played extra time.

*What smells horrible, runs about all day and lies around at night with its tongue hanging out?* One of Aerobic Al's old trainers.

*What's the best way to win a race?* Run faster than everyone else!

**HENRY'S DAD:** Henry has got into the football team.
**AL'S DAD:** What position does he play?
**HENRY'S DAD:** He's left back in the changing room.

Twenty-two ants were playing football in a saucer. One ant says to the other, "We'll have to play better than this tomorrow – we're playing in the cup."

# HORRID HOLIDAY HOWLERS

*Who on the beach has the biggest sunhat?*
The person with
the biggest head.

*What do witches use in the summer?*
Suntan potion.

*Why was Greedy Graham doing the backstroke
after lunch?*
Because you're not supposed to swim
on a full stomach.

*Why didn't Beefy Bert enjoy
his water skiing holiday?*
He couldn't find a sloping lake.

**HENRY'S DAD:** Are
the rooms here quiet?
**HOTEL MANAGER:**
Yes, sir, it's only the guests
that are noisy.

**HENRY'S MUM:** How much
do you charge for a week's stay?
**HOTEL MANAGER:** I don't know,
no one's ever stayed that long.

**ANXIOUS ANDREW:**
Do these ships sink often?
**CAPTAIN:** No, only once.

# GLOBE-TROTTING GIGGLES

*What's a volcano?*
A mountain with hiccups.

*What makes the Tower of Pisa lean?*
It doesn't eat much.

*Which country has the thinnest people?*
Finland.

*What's the coldest country in the world?*
Chile.

*What's the coldest city in Germany?*
Brrrr-lin.

*Where do sheep go on holiday?*
The Baa-hamas.

*What stays in one corner, but*
*can go all around the world?*
A postage stamp.

*Where do elephants go on holiday?*
Tuscany.

*Where do cows go on holiday?*
Moo Zealand.

Henry! Stop saying
'Moo'.

**OK, Maggie**
**Moo Moo.**

Don't call me that!

*Where do cats go on holiday?*
The Canary Islands.

# ANIMALS IN THE SUN

*Why did the monkey lie on the sunbed?*
To get an orangu-tan.

*What's grey, has four legs and a trunk?*
A mouse going on holiday.

*What's brown, has four legs and a trunk?*
A mouse coming back from holiday.

*What do you get when you cross
an elephant with a fish?*
Swimming trunks.

*What do bees say in summer?*
'Swarm.

*Why aren't elephants allowed on the beach?*
In case their trunks fall down.

*Where would you weigh a whale?*
At a whale-weigh station.

*Why did the crab
go to jail?*
He kept pinching
things.

*How did the frog cross the Channel?*
By hoppercraft.

*What do horses suffer from in the summertime?*
Neigh fever.

# HAIRY HUMOUR

**PATIENT:** Doctor, doctor, my hair's coming out. Can you give me something to keep it in?
**DOCTOR:** Certainly – how about a plastic bag?

*Why did Beefy Bert take his comb to the dentist?*
Because its teeth were falling out.

**PATIENT:** Doctor, doctor, I keep thinking I'm a dog.
**DOCTOR:** Lie down on this couch and I'll examine you.
**PATIENT:** I'm not allowed. I might make it all hairy!

**BARBER:** How would you like your hair cut, sir?

**MR MOSSY:** Could you leave one side long and cut one side short, with a crooked fringe at the front and bald patches on the top?

**BARBER:** Oh dear, I don't think I can manage that, sir.

**MR MOSSY:** Why not? You did last time.

**PATIENT:** Doctor, doctor, my hair seems to be getting thinner.

**DOCTOR:** Why do you want fat hair?

*Who can shave twenty-five times a day and still have a beard?*
A barber.

*Three men fall out of a boat but only two get their hair wet. Why?*
Because the third man is bald!

# SIZZLING SNACKS

*What is a meatball?*
A dance in the
butcher's shop.

*How do you make a really good milkshake?*
Tell it a scary story.

*What do you call a banana split
when you've dropped it from
the top of a skyscraper on to
the pavement below?*
A banana splat.

*What do sheep enjoy on a sunny day?*
Having a baa-becue.

*How do monkeys toast bread?*
They put it under the gorilla.

**RICH AUNT RUBY:**
Excuse me, waiter, is
there spaghetti on
the menu?
**WAITER:** No, madam,
I wiped it off.

*Why can't you starve in the desert?*
Because of the sand which is there.

*Have you ever seen a man-eating tiger?*
No, but I've seen a man eating chicken.

Greedy Graham walked into a library, and
said to the librarian, "Cod and chips, please."
"This isn't a fish and chip shop," said the
librarian. "It's a library."
"Cod and chips, please," whispered
Greedy Graham.

# FAMILY FUNNIES

**MOODY MARGARET:** I'm homesick.
**MUM:** But this is your home.
**MOODY MARGARET:** I know, and I'm sick of it.

*My dad just opened a sweet shop.*
I bet he makes a mint.

Did you hear about the well-behaved little boy? Whenever he was good, his dad gave him 10p and a pat on the head. By the time he was sixteen, he had £786 and a flat head.

**WEEPY WILLIAM:**
Do you notice any change
in me?
**MUM:** No. Why?
**WEEPY WILLIAM:**
I just swallowed 5p. Waaaa!

Daddy, there's a man with a beard at the
door.
**DAD:** Tell him I've got one already!

**DAD:** Who broke this window?
**HORRID HENRY:** It was
Peter, Dad. I threw an apple at
him and he ducked.

**HORRID HENRY:** Dad, could
you do my homework for me?
**DAD:** No, it wouldn't be right.
**HORRID HENRY:** But you
could at least try.

# ZANY ZOOS AND BIZARRE BEASTS

*What has an elephant's trunk, a lion's mane and a baboon's bottom?*
A zoo.

*What's black and white and red all over?*
A shy zebra.

*Where do baby apes sleep?*
In apricots.

*What kind of bird can write?*
A PENguin.

*Why didn't the viper*
*viper nose?*
Because the adder
adder handkerchief.

*What's long and green and goes hith?*
*A snake with a lisp.*

**GRIZZLY BEAR:** Could I have a
lemonade.......and a chocolate muffin?
**WAITRESS:** Why the big pause?
**GRIZZLY BEAR:** I don't know.
My father had them too.

*Why does a hummingbird hum?*
It doesn't know the words.

*What do you give a gorilla for his birthday?*
I don't know, but let's hope he likes it!

*What do you call a camel with three humps?*
Humphrey.

*What do you call a camel with no humps?*
A horse.

*Why didn't the old lady run away from the lion?*
She knew it was a man-eater.

*Why couldn't the leopard escape from the zoo?*
It was always spotted.

*What sort of ape can fly?*
A hot air baboon.

*What animal are you like when you have a bath?*
A bear!

# KNOCK, KNOCK! AUTUMN'S ON ITS WAY

Knock, knock!
Who's there?
*You.*
You who?
*Did you call?*

    *Knock, knock!*
    Who's there?
    *Dishes.*
    Dishes who?
    *Dishes a very bad joke.*

        *Knock, knock!*
        Who's there?
        *Repeat.*
        Repeat who?
        *Who, who, who!*

*Knock, knock!*
Who's there?
*Cow-go.*
Cow-go who?
*No, cow go MOO!*

*Knock, knock!*
Who's there?
*Europe.*
Europe who?
*Europe up early for a lazybones.*

*Knock, knock!*
Who's there?
*Ralph.*
Ralph who?
*Ralph, Ralph – I'm just a puppy.*

# AUTUMN

Oh no!
It's so unfair! Autumn
means ... school.
Aaarrrrggghhhh.
Grisly grub school
dinners and spelling tests and
Miss Battle-Axe and her evil eye
and big yellow teeth and pointy
fingers. Eeeek.

Well, let all my great jokes
cheer you up. Your teacher will
be putty in your hands once
you've learned my Horrible
History Howlers or my amazing
Ghostly Giggles.

And don't forget, autumn means
Halloween and loads and loads
and loads of sweets! Yippee!
Chocolate Hairballs here I come!

# AUTUMN ANTICS

Why do spiders like
the Internet?
Because of all
the websites.

What do you call a man who walks
through autumn leaves?
Russell.

How does an elephant get down from a tree?
He sits on a leaf and waits for autumn.

What's the best way to make a fire
using two sticks?
Make sure one of them is a match!

What do you call a jacket that's on fire?
A blazer.

*What did one autumn leaf say to the other?*
I'm falling for you.

*How do you mend a broken pumpkin?*
With a pumpkin patch.

**PERFECT PETER:**
Am I too late for the
bonfire?
**HORRID HENRY:**
No, just jump up on
the sticks. There's room
next to that guy.

*What do you get if you
cross a dinosaur with a
firework?*
A dino-mite.

*Why did Beefy Bert hurt himself raking up leaves?*
He fell out of the tree.

# BACK TO SCHOOL

### Boo - hiss!

**SOUR SUSAN:** What shall we play today?

**MOODY MARGARET:** Let's play school. I'll be the teacher.

**SOUR SUSAN:** OK! And I'll be absent!

*What's Moody Margaret's favourite day of the week?*
Moanday.

*Why did the jellybean go to school?*
Because he wanted to be a Smartie.

*Why did the boy take a ladder to school?*
Because it was a high school.

*Why did the headmaster marry the school cleaner?*
She swept him off his feet.

*What was the blackbird doing in the school library?* Looking for bookworms.

*What do you call an ant who skips school?*
A tru-ant.

**ANXIOUS ANDREW:** I keep thinking I'm the school bell.
**NURSE NEEDLE:** Take these tablets and if they don't help, give me a ring in the morning.

*Why did the boy take his car to school?*
To drive his teacher up the wall.

*What's the difference between Miss Battle-Axe and a steam train?*
One says, "Spit out that chewing gum," and the other says, "Choo-choo!"

**MR NERDON:** Ralph, don't hum while you're working.
**RUDE RALPH:** I'm not working, Sir, just humming.

# SCHOOL GRUB GROSS-OUT

**RUDE RALPH:** How do you think they keep flies out of the school canteen?

**HORRID HENRY:** They probably let them taste the food!

**MOODY MARGARET:** Oh good, we're having salad for school dinner today.

**SOUR SUSAN:** How do you know it's salad?

**MOODY MARGARET:** Well, I can't smell anything burning.

**GREEDY GRAHAM:** I'm doing really well at school.

**MUM:** That's wonderful.

**GREEDY GRAHAM:** Yes, today I was first in the dinner queue.

*What's a mushroom?*
The place where they keep the school dinners.

**GREEDY GRAHAM:** Why is there a button in my lunch?

**GREASY GRETA:** It's off the jacket potatoes.

**COOKERY TEACHER:** Graham, what are the best things to put in a pie?

**GREEDY GRAHAM:** Teeth!

# TERRIBLE TEACHER JOKES

*What did the teacher say
to the naughty bee?*
Bee-hive yourself.

What are the only two good
things about being a teacher?

**MISS BATTLE-AXE:**
July and August.

**MISS BATTLE-AXE:** We call you
"the wonder child" in the staff room.
**RUDE RALPH:** Why's that?
**MISS BATTLE-AXE:** Because we all
wonder when you're going to wash!

**MR NERDON:** Henry, you're late for school again. What is it this time?

**HORRID HENRY:** I sprained my ankle, Sir.

**MR NERDON:** What a lame excuse!

**MRS ODDBOD AT ASSEMBLY:** Last night someone broke into the school stationery cupboard and stole a load of blunt pencils. The police described the theft as pointless.

*What's the worst school trip?*
The trip to the headteacher's office.

*Why did the teacher wear dark glasses?*
Because she had such a bright class.

*What do you get when you cross a teacher with a vampire?*
Lots of blood tests.

# CLASSROOM CORNER

**MISS BATTLE-AXE:** What's the most important thing to remember in a chemistry lesson?

**GREEDY GRAHAM:** Don't lick the spoon.

**MISS BATTLE-AXE:** Henry, didn't you hear me call you?

**HORRID HENRY:** Yes, but you're always telling us not to answer back.

**MUM:** What did you learn at school today?

**HORRID HENRY:** Not enough. I have to go back tomorrow.

**MUM:** I told you not to eat cake before supper.

**GREEDY GRAHAM:** But Mum, I'm just doing my Maths homework. If you take an eighth of a cake from a whole cake, how much is left?

*If a bottle of lemonade became a teacher, what subject would it teach?* Fizzical education.

**MISS BATTLE-AXE:** Can anyone name a bird that doesn't build its own nest?

**DIZZY DAVE:** The cuckoo.

**MISS BATTLE-AXE:** That's right! How did you know that?

**DIZZY DAVE:** Because cuckoos live in clocks.

# WORDY WHEEZES

**MISS BATTLE-AXE:** What does the word 'abundance' mean?

**GREEDY GRAHAM:** Lots of dancing cakes?

**MISS BATTLE-AXE:** Bert, what do we call the outside of a tree?

**BEEFY BERT:** I dunno, Miss.

**MISS BATTLE-AXE:** Bark, you silly boy, bark!

**BEEFY BERT:** Woof woof!

**MISS BATTLE-AXE:** Who can tell me what a cartoon is?

**SINGING SORAYA:** A song you sing in a car?

**MISS LOVELY:**
What's the plural of mouse?
**TIDY TED:** Mice.
**MISS LOVELY:**
What's the plural of baby?
**TIDY TED:** Twins.

**MISS BATTLE-AXE:**
Graham, what is 'can't' short for?
**GREEDY GRAHAM:** Cannot.
**MISS BATTLE-AXE:** And what is
"don't" short for?
**GREEDY GRAHAM:**
Doughnut!

**MISS BATTLE-AXE:**
What does minimum mean?
**DIZZY DAVE:** A very
small mother?

*How does Horrid Henry send funny messages?*
By tee-hee mail.

# HORRIBLE HISTORY HOWLERS

**MISS BATTLE-AXE:**
Where did Napoleon
keep his armies?
**RUDE RALPH:**
Up his sleevies?

**LAZY LINDA:**
I wish we lived in the olden days.
**MISS BATTLE-AXE:** Why?
**LAZY LINDA:** Then there wouldn't
be so much history to learn.

**MISS BATTLE-AXE:** During which
battle was Lord Nelson killed?
**CLEVER CLARE:** His last one!

**MISS BATTLE-AXE:** What came after the Stone Age and the Bronze Age?

> **GREEDY GRAHAM:** The sausage!

> **MISS BATTLE-AXE:** What's the difference between the death rate in Elizabethan times and the death rate nowadays?

**CLEVER CLARE:** It's still the same — one death per person.

**MISS BATTLE-AXE:** Who invented fractions?

**MOODY MARGARET:** Henry the Eighth.

*Why do Egyptian pyramids have doorbells?*
So you can toot-n-come in.

**MISS BATTLE-AXE:**
Who was the fastest
runner in history?
**AEROBIC AL:**
Adam – because
he came first in the
human race!

**MISS BATTLE-AXE:** Tell me
something important that didn't exist 100
years ago.
**HORRID HENRY:** Me!

# MERRY MATHS

*What's the fastest way to count cows?*
Using a cowculator

**MISS BATTLE-AXE:** If you had 10p, and you asked your dad for another 10p, how much would you have?

**ANXIOUS ANDREW:** Er…
10p, Miss.

**MISS BATTLE-AXE:** You don't know your arithmetic, Andrew!

**ANXIOUS ANDREW:** You don't know my dad, Miss.

**MISS BATTLE-AXE:**
If you add 26 and
301, then double it
and divide by 6,
what do you get?
**HORRID HENRY:**
The wrong answer.

*Why was the Maths book puzzled?*
Because it had a lot of questions.

*Why was the zero punished?*
Because it was noughty.

**MISS BATTLE-AXE:** How can
you make so many mistakes in
one maths class?
**SOUR SUSAN:** Because I get
here early.

*What kind of tree is good at Maths?*
A geometry!

# RIBTICKLING TESTS

**HORRID HENRY:** I don't think I deserved zero for this test.

**MISS BATTLE-AXE:** I don't either, but it's the lowest I can give.

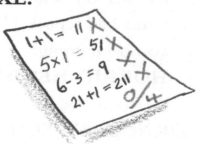

*How did the dinosaur pass his exam?*
With extinction.

**DAD:** Were your test results good?

**HORRID HENRY:** Yes and no.

**DAD:** What do you mean, "Yes and no"?

**HORRID HENRY:** YES, my test results were NO good.

**BRAINY BRIAN:** Let's have a race to say our tables.

**CLEVER CLARE:** *Our tables*. I win!

**MUM:** All your teachers have given you a bad report, Henry. What have you been doing?

**HORRID HENRY:** Nothing, Mum.

## DRACULA'S SCHOOL REPORT

Reading: *better in the dark*

Writing: *upside down*

Cricket: *shows promise as a bat*

# HALLOWEEN CACKLES

*What do birds say at Halloween?*
Trick or tweet!

*Why do witches all look the same?*
So you can't tell which witch is which.

*What kind of monster has the best hearing?*
The eeriest!

*Did you hear about the vampire*
*who needed a drink?*
He was bloodthirsty.

*Knock, knock!*
Who's there?
*Ivan.*
Ivan who?
*Ivan to suck your blood!*

*Why do vampires like thick books?*
They like stories they can really get their teeth into.

*What goes "Flap, flap! Bite, bite! Ouch, ouch!"*
Dracula with toothache.

*What do you call a witch's garage?*
A broom cupboard.

*What was the name of the little witch's brother?*
He was cauld-Ron.

*How many witches does it take to change a light bulb?*
Only one, but she changes it into a toad.

# GHOSTLY GIGGLES

*What did the mother ghost say to the naughty baby ghost?*
Don't spook until you're spooken to.

*What do you get if you cross a ghost with a packet of crisps?*
Snacks that go crunch in the night.

*Why can't ghosts tell fibs?*
Because you can see right through them.

*What do you get if you cross a footballer with a ghost?*
A ghoulie.

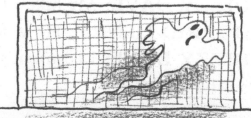

Horrid Henry went to a Halloween party with a sheet on his head.
"Are you a ghost?" asked Rude Ralph.
"No, I'm an unmade bed."

*What's a baby ghost's favourite game?*
Peek-a-BOO!

*Why was the bowl of soup so scary?*
It was scream of tomato.

*How do monsters count to twenty-three?*
On their fingers.

**DIZZY DAVE:** My bike's haunted.
**HORRID HENRY:** How do you know?
**DIZZY DAVE:** Because it's got spooks on the wheels.

# KNOCK, KNOCK!
# WINTER'S COMING

*Knock, knock!*
Who's there?
*Worm.*
Worm who?
*Worm in there,*
*but cold outside.*

  *Knock, knock!*
  Who's there?
  *Aunt.*
  Aunt who?
  *Aunt these jokes terrible.*

    *Knock, knock!*
    Who's there?
    *Nana.*
    Nana who?
    *Nana your business.*

*Knock, knock!*
Who's there?
*Olivia.*
Olivia who?
*Olivia, but I've lost my key*

> *Knock, knock!*
> Who's there?
> *Beezer.*
> Beezer who?
> *Beezer black and yellow.*

*Knock, knock!*
Who's there?
*Mickey.*
Mickey who?
*Mickey won't fit, that's why I'm knocking.*

> *Knock, knock!*
> Who's there?
> *Snow.*
> Snow who?
> *Snow use, I've forgotten my keys.*

# WINTER

I LOVE winter! Snowballs and weather so cold and wet and miserable there's no way Mum and Dad can

drag me on nature walks so I get to stay warm and snug on the sofa watching telly! And of course winter means ... Christmas! Don't let Santa get away with not giving you all those great presents you deserve – especially those Bugle Blast Boots he forgot last year. And remember to make loads of noise on New Year's Eve!

# WINTRY WHEEZES

What did one snowman say to the other?
"Can you smell carrots?"

What do you call a snowman
on a sunny day?
A puddle.

What food do you get when you cross a
snowman with a polar bear?
A brrr–grrr.

How do you know when there's
a snowman in your bed?
You wake up wet!

*What do you get if you cross
a snowman and a shark?*
Frost bite!

*Why don't mountains get cold in the winter?*
Because they wear snow caps.

*What goes: Now you see me, now you
don't, now you see me, now you don't?*
A snowman on a zebra crossing.

*What sort of ball doesn't bounce?*
A snowball.

# CHILLY CHUCKLES

*What's white, furry and smells minty?*
A polo bear.

*How do sheep keep warm in the winter?*
They turn on the central bleating.

*What animal would you get if you*
*tied ice cubes around your neck?*
A chin chiller.

*What do you call*
*a polar bear in*
*a jungle?*
Lost!

*How does Jack Frost travel about?*
On his icicle.

*What do you get if you cross*
*a goldfish and an ice cube?*
A cold fish.

*Why are igloos round?*
So polar bears can't hide in the corners.

*What falls in winter but doesn't get hurt?*
Snow.

*Why shouldn't you ice skate on a full stomach?*
Because it's easier on an ice rink.

# JOLLY CHRISTMAS JESTS

**BRAINY BRIAN:** What's the difference between an elephant and a postbox?

**BEEFY BERT:** I dunno.
**BRAINY BRIAN:** Well, I'm not asking you to post my Christmas cards.

*What did the big cracker say to the little cracker?*
My pop is bigger than yours.

*What did one angel say to the other?*
Halo there.

What do angry mice send to each other
at Christmas?
Cross mouse cards.

What happened to the
thief who stole a
Christmas calendar?
He got 12 months!

What did Adam say on
the day before Christmas?
It's Christmas, Eve!

Knock, knock!
Who's there?
Holly.
Holly who?
Holly-days are here again.

Why is it always cold at Christmas?
Because it's Decembrrrrrrr!

*What's the difference between the ordinary
alphabet and the Christmas alphabet?*
The Christmas alphabet has No-el.

*What is green, covered with tinsel
and goes ribbet ribbet?*
Mistle-toad!

*Why are Christmas trees like bad knitters?*
They both drop their needles!

# FUNNY
# FOOD

**PERFECT PETER:** Can I have a canary
for Christmas?
**MUM:** No, you can have turkey
like the rest of us.

*Who is never
hungry at
Christmas?*
The turkey –
he's always
stuffed.

*How does good King Wenceslas
like his pizzas?*
Deep pan, crisp and even.

*What do you get if you cross a Christmas tree with an apple?*
A pine-apple.

*What do snowmen like for lunch?*
Icebergers.

*We had grandma for Christmas dinner.*
Really, we had turkey!

*What's the definition of a balanced diet?*
A Christmas cake in each hand.

# COMICAL CAROLS

*What do elephants sing at Christmas?*
No-elephants, No-elephants…

*How do sheep greet each other at Christmas?*
A merry Christmas to ewe.

*What's Tarzan's favourite Christmas song?*
Jungle Bells.

*What do they sing in the desert
at Christmas time?*
"Oh camel ye
faithful…"

*What Christmas carol
do Horrid Henry's
parents like?*
Silent night.

*What's a gorilla's favourite
Christmas song?*
King Kong
merrily
on high.

*What did the guests sing at
Father Christmas's party?*
Freeze a jolly good fellow!

*What's a hairdresser's favourite Christmas song?*
Oh, comb all ye faithful.

*What musical instrument was the fisherman
given for Christmas?*
A cast-a-net.

*Knock, knock!*
Who's there?
*Wayne.*
Wayne who?
*(Sing) "Wayne in a manger, no crib for a bed."*

# SANTA SNIGGERS

*What is Father Christmas's wife called?*
Mary Christmas.

*Who delivers the cat's*
*Christmas presents?*
Santa Paws.

*Why does Father*
*Christmas go down the chimney?*
Because it soots him.

*How many chimneys does Father Christmas*
*go down on Christmas Eve?*
Stacks!

*Why is it difficult to keep a secret at the North Pole?*
Because your teeth chatter.

*Why does Santa like to work in the garden?*
Because he likes to hoe hoe hoe.

*Why does Santa wear bright red braces?*
To hold his trousers up.

*What does a cat on the beach have in common with Christmas?*
Sandy claws.

*What type of cars do Santa's elves drive?*
TOY-otas.

*What do elves learn at school?*
The Elf-abet.

*How do elves get tummy ache?*
By goblin their food.

*What does Santa do when his elves are naughty?*
He gives them the sack.

*Who looks after Father Christmas when he's ill?*
The National Elf Service.

# REINDEER RIBTICKLERS

What do you call
a reindeer wearing ear
muffs?
Anything you want
because he can't hear
you!

What you call a reindeer with only three legs?
Eileen.

What do you call a reindeer with only one eye?
No idea.

What do you call a reindeer with
no legs and only one eye?
Still no idea.

*Where would you find a reindeer with no legs?*
Where you left it.

*What reindeer can jump higher than a house?*
All of them – a house can't jump.

*How do you get milk*
*from a reindeer?*
Rob its fridge
and run like mad.

*Why do reindeer scratch themselves?*
Because no one else knows where
they itch!

*Why do reindeers wear fur coats?*
Because they'd look silly in plastic macs.

# KNOCK, KNOCK!
# LET THE
# NEW YEAR IN

*Knock, knock!*
Who's there?
*Luke.*
Luke who?
*Luke through the*
*window and you'll see.*

*Knock, knock!*
Who's there?
*Howard.*
Howard who?
*Howard you like it if I made*
*you stand out in the cold?*

102

*Knock, knock!*
Who's there?
*Doris.*
Doris who?
*Doris closed, that's why I'm knocking.*

*Knock, knock!*
Who's there?
*Harry.*
Harry who?
*Harry up and open the door.*

*Knock, knock!*
Who's there?
*Police.*
Police who?
*Police open the door.*

*Knock, knock!*
Who's there?
*Police.*
Police who?
*POLICE STOP TELLING THESE AWFUL KNOCK, KNOCK JOKES!*

Well, that's it, guys. I am out of jokes. Lucky for me I got 365, that's 'cause I am the best, most amazing and totally brilliant...

Actually you only have 364 jokes, Henry.

**Liar!**

I counted, Henry. It's only 364.

Out of my way, worm!
You're wrong, you
wormy worm toad,
I've counted them
too, watch, 362 ...
363 ... 364 ... 364...
Ooops.

Okay, listen up, everyone.
I need one more great joke.
Help me out!!!!

Send your absolute best joke in
to the Horrid Henry website at:

www.horridhenry.co.uk

# HORRID HENRY'S
# PURPLE HAND
# GANG
# JOKE BOOK

# CONTENTS

# Hello from Henry

Hey, everyone! I thought my other joke books had the horridest, wickedest, funniest and rudest jokes ever. But who knew my Purple Hand Gang would tell me so many GREAT jokes? Wow! Thanks for doing all the hard work, guys. I think I'll just stomp downstairs and drive Mum and Dad crazy with a few of these zingers. Way to go, gang. The Purple Hand Gang rules!

*Henry*

# MY TOP PURPLE JOKES

*What's purple and fixes pipes?*
A plum-er.

*Why did the elephant paint itself purple?*
So it could hide in the plum tree.

*Why are elephants big and grey?*
If they were small and purple
they'd be grapes.

*What's purple and sounds like an ape?*
A grape.

*What's purple and barks at people?*
A Grape Dane.

*What happens when you drop
a purple rock in
the Red Sea?*
It gets wet.

HENRY: There's a horrible big purple thing on your face!
DAD: Help! What is it?
HENRY: Your nose!

*What's purple, brown and hairy?* Blackberry jam on toast stuck to the carpet.

*What colour is a burp?*
Burple

# FAVOURITE JOKES FROM MY FANS

*What do you get when you cross a cow and a werewolf?*
A burger that bites back.

Snash!
Snash!

*Did you hear about the fight outside the chippie last night?*
Two fish got battered!

*What did Mummy corn say to Baby corn?*
Where's Pop corn?

*Waiter, Waiter, why is there a footprint on my cake?*
Because you said step on it.

*Why didn't the elephant board his plane?*
Because it wasn't a jumbo.

*Which ghost stops goals?*
A ghoulkeeper.

*Which are the three most famous poles?*
North, South and Tad.

*What do you call a daft dinosaur?*
Idiotsaurus.

*Why are bananas so good
at gymnastics?*
They are great at doing the splits.

*What's a polygon?*
A dead parrot.

*Where did the spaghetti dance?*
At the meatball.

*What do you call a
lion without any eyes?*
Lon.

*Doctor, Doctor, I only
have 50 seconds to live.*
Just give me a
minute.

*Knock knock.*
Who's there?
*Justin.*
Justin who?
*Justin in time to let me in, toad.*

*What do you get when you cross a cat and a parrot?*
A carrot.

*Who is a penguin's favourite aunt?*
Aunt Arctica.

*Why did the boy put sugar on his pillow?*
He wanted to have sweet dreams.

*What do you call a donkey with one eye and three legs?*

A winky wonky donkey.

*Why are insects clever?*

Because they always know when you're having a picnic.

*What do you get when you cross a bomb and a bad smell?*

A stinkbomb.

*Doctor, Doctor, I can't sleep at night.*
Lie on the edge of your bed and
you'll soon drop off.

*What goes black white
black white black white?*
A penguin rolling down a hill.

*What goes black white
black white black white,
HA HA?*
The penguin that
pushed him.

*Why did the mushroom enjoy the party so much?*
Because he's a fungi.

*What was the magical secret agent called?*
James Wand.

*Did I tell you the joke about butter?*
I'd better not in case you spread it.

*Waiter, Waiter, will my pizza be long?*
No, sir, it'll be round.

*Why are adults always complaining?*
Because they are groan ups.

*Who did Frankenstein
take to the party?*
His ghoulfriend.

*What do you call a scared octopus?*
An octopussy.

*How does a cowboy ride into town on Friday,
stay for three days and ride
out on Friday?*
His horse is called Friday!

What's an astronaut's favourite
place on the keyboard?
The spacebar.

What do hedgehogs
like to eat?
Prickled onions.

What do mother penguins tell their
children when they go out?
Beak careful.

Why does a cow have a bell?
Because its horns don't work.

*Why did the cow cross the road?*
To get to the udder side.

*Why did the cow cross the road again?*
It wanted to see a moooooovie.

*What do you call a scared biscuit?*
A cowardy custard cream.

*What do you get when you cross
a sheep with a kangaroo?*
A woolly jumper.

*Knock knock.*
Who's there?
*Cash.*
Cash who?
*No thanks, I prefer peanuts.*

*Why did the biscuit
go to the doctors?*
Because he felt
crummy.

*What's the difference between roast beef and pea soup?*
Anyone can roast beef but nobody can pea soup.

*Why don't leopards cheat in exams?*
They know they'll be spotted.

*What do you call a man with a seagull on his head?*
Cliff.

*Waiter, Waiter, there's a small slug in my salad.*
Sorry, Madam, would you like a bigger one?

*What do you call a woodpecker with no beak?*
A headbanger.

MISS BATTLE-AXE: Today I want you
to write an essay on a goldfish.
RUDE RALPH: I can't do that.
MISS BATTLE-AXE: Why not?
RUDE RALPH: Because I don't
have any waterproof ink.

*Why is Europe like a frying pan?*
It has Greece at the bottom.

*Doctor, Doctor, I feel like a cow.*
Sit there and don't moooooooove.

*What is a ghost's favourite food?*
Spookhetti.

The three bears came home. Daddy Bear
said, "Who's been eating my porridge?"
and Mummy Bear said, "Who's been
eating my porridge?"
and Baby Bear said, "Never mind
about the porridge, who's nicked
the telly!"

*What do you call
a computer superhero?*
A screen saver.

*How do you get a baby astronaut to sleep?*
Rocket.

*Why couldn't the orange run up the hill?*
It ran out of juice.

*Why can't a monster's head be
12 inches long?*
Because then it would be a foot.

*Where do wasps go
when they're hurt?*
To the waspital.

*What do you call a sleeping bull?*
A bulldozer.

*A butcher is two metres tall and wears
size thirteen shoes. What does he weigh?*
Meat.

*What do you get when you cross*
*Dr Frankenstein with a pig?*
Frankenswine.

*What do computers eat?*
Microchips.

*What do you call a lion with toothache?*
Rory.

*What does an octopus wear when it's cold?*
A coat of arms.

*Where do you catch a flying pig?*
At the airpork.

*What do you call a fish with no eye?*
A fsh.

MISS BATTLE-AXE: Name the
four seasons.
GREEDY GRAHAM: Salt, pepper,
mustard and vinegar.

*What's the cleverest
species of dinosaur?*
A Thesaurus.

*Who shouted knickers at the big bad wolf?*
Little rude riding hood.

*Why did the boy carry a clock
and a bird on Halloween?*
For tick or tweet.

*Knock knock.*
Who's there?
*Bacon.*
Bacon who?
*Bacon a cake for your birthday.*

*What do you get when you cross
a computer with an elephant?*
Lots of memory.

*What did the frog order at the fast
food restaurant?*
French flies and a diet croak.

*What goes up the stairs
but never moves?*
A carpet.

*How do you make a fruit punch?*
Give it boxing lessons.

*What do you call a man with a map*
*on his head?*
Miles.

*Who gives presents to children,*
*then gobbles them up?*
Santa Jaws.

*How do snails keep their shells so shiny?*
They use snail varnish.

*What do witches
put on their hair?*
Scare spray.

*Which painting is never happy?*
The Moaning Lisa.

*What are the werewolves' cousins called?*
The whywolf, the whatwolf and the
whenwolf.

*Can I tell you a joke about a wall?*
Yes please.
*No, because you'll never get over it.*

A man came round to our house asking for donations for the local swimming pool. I gave him a glass of water!

*What does a ghost call his mum and dad?*
Transparents.

*What's the Earth's favourite bit of a pizza?*
The crust.

*What do cows eat for breakfast?*
MOOOuesli.

*Which two letters are bad for your teeth?*
DK.

*What does a dentist do on a rollercoaster?*
He braces himself.

*What did the elf use to make himself taller?*
Elf raising flour.

*Why was the skeleton afraid of the dog?*
Because dogs like bones!

*What do you get when you cross*
*a pig and a woodchopper?*
Pork chops.

*What do you call James Bond in the bath?*
Bubble O Seven.

*What do you call a woman with two toilets on her head?*
Lulu.

DAD: I hope you're not talking in class any more.
HORRID HENRY: I'm not talking any more, I'm talking the same amount.

*I saw Esau sitting on a see-saw.*
*How many s's in that?*
There aren't any s's in THAT!

*Doctor, Doctor, I've got a strawberry growing on my head.*
Well, put some cream on it.

*What runs but has no legs?*
Water.

*Waiter, Waiter, do
you serve fish?*
Sit down, Sir,
we serve anyone.

*What did the plumber say to his wife
when their marriage ended?*
It's over flow.

*What's the sweetest
insect?*
A humbug.

*Knock knock.*
Who's there?
*Egbert.*
Egbert who?
*Egbert no bacon.*

*What do you
call a rooster that
wakes you up at
the same time every
morning?*
An alarm cluck.

*What do you
call a skeleton
snake?*
A rattler.

*What's the difference between an African
elephant and an Indian elephant?*
About 6,000 kilometres.

MUM: Shall I put the kettle on?
DAD: No, I prefer the dress you're wearing now.

LADY: Can I try that dress on in the window?
SHOPKEEPER: No way, try it on in the changing room.

*Doctor, Doctor, I think I'm shrinking.*
Well, you'll have to be a little patient.

*What happened to the cat that
ate a ball of wool?*
She had mittens.

*What has 22 legs, 11 heads and 2 wings?*
A football team.

*A bee just stung me on my arm.*
Which one?
*I don't know, they all look the same to me.*

*Why did the sheep cross the road?*
It wanted to go to the baaaarbers.

*What do you call a bee that lives in a graveyard?*
A zom-bee.

*What cheese is made backwards?*
Edam.

*Doctor, Doctor, I keep thinking I'm a canary.*
Perch yourself down and I'll tweet you in a
minute.

*What did the ghost teacher say to
her pupils?*
Look at the board – I'm going
to go through it again.

*What do you get when you dial 340273589
23759235872935873589857?*
A sore finger.

*Why do hens watch TV?*
For hentertainment.

*Why is my brother built upside down?*
Because his nose runs and his feet smell.

*What did one volcano say to the other volcano?*
Do you lava me like I lava you?

*What do you get when you cross a cow,*
*a sheep and a baby goat?*
The Milky Baa kid.

*Why did the submarine go red?*
Because it saw the ship's bottom.

*What did the parrot take for his headache?*
Parrotcetemol.

*A horse went up to two cows and said,*
*"Excuse me, where are the toilets?"*
"That's amazing," said one cow to the
other, "a horse that can speak."

*What do you call a man*
*with a tree growing out*
*of his head?*
Edward.

*Why did a man with*
*one hand cross the road?*
To get to the second
hand shop.

One day a man was walking down the
street with a penguin. A policeman saw
them and told the man to take the
penguin to the zoo. The next day the
policeman saw the man again with the
penguin, and said, "I thought I told you to
take the penguin to the zoo." The man said,
"I did, and we had such fun that
I'm taking him to the cinema today."

*What's black when you buy it, red when you use it and grey when you throw it away?*
Coal.

*What's a sheep's favourite snack?*
Chocolate baaaaaars.

*There were three cookies in the jar last night and now there's only one. What's your excuse?*
It was dark so I must have missed it!

*What do you call a man who likes fishing?*
Rod.

*What did the chick say when his mum*
*laid an orange?*
Look what marmalade.

*What does an alien from Mars like to eat?*
Martian-mallows.

*Why do zebras like old movies?*
Because they are black and white.

*What happened to the wooden car with the*
*wooden wheels and the wooden engine?*
It wooden go.

*What did the teacher say when the horse walked into the classroom?*
Why the long face?

*What are a monster's favourite fairground rides?*
The helter skeleton and the roller ghoster.

*How does a dog stop the DVD player?*
He presses the paws button.

A guest in a posh hotel says to the waiter, "Can I order two boiled eggs, one undercooked and runny and one overcooked and tough, with some rubbery bacon and burnt toast."

The waiter said, "Sir, we can't serve such a dreadful breakfast!"

"Why not?" the guest replied. "That's what I got here yesterday!"

*Knock knock.*
Who's there?
*A dare.*
A dare who?
*A dare once, but I'm bald now.*

*Why do dogs run round in circles?*
It's hard to run in squares.

*What do you call a skunk that's disappeared?*
Ex-stinked.

*What has a bed but never sleeps?*
A river.

*Why did the bald man stick his head
out of the window?*
To get some fresh hair.

*Which travels faster — heat or cold?*
Heat, because you can catch a cold.

*How do you make a jacket last?*
Make the trousers first.

*Why is history like a fruitcake?*
It's full of dates.

*What did the scarf say to the hat?*
You go on ahead and I'll hang around.

*What comes once in a minute, twice in a moment, but never in a thousand years?*
The letter M.

*What smells worse than a skunk?*
Two skunks.

*Did you hear about the wolves'*
*all-night party?*
It was a howling success.

*When do birds celebrate their dads?*
On feather's day.

*What do you call an animal that*
*talks too much?*
A yak.

*Why did Santa have to close his factory?*
For elf and safety.

*What do you get when you cross a cow
and an earthquake?*
A milkshake.

*Why don't oysters share?*
Because they're shellfish.

*What do you call a parrot with no wings?*
A walkie talkie.

*How do you catch a rabbit?*
Hide behind a tree and
make a noise like a carrot.

*What can you serve but can't eat?*
Tennis balls.

*What did the lion say when he saw two men in a car?*
Yum, yum, meals on wheels.

*Why did the robber take a bath?*
He wanted to make a clean getaway.

*Why did the overweight man throw his wallet in the bin?*
He wanted to lose a couple of pounds.

*Which vehicle is the same going*
*backwards or forwards?*
Racecar.

*What's the best place for a mouse*
*to leave its boat?*
The hickory dickory dock.

*Why was the broom late for breakfast?*
It overswept.

How can you swallow a plug?
Gulp backwards.

What goes 'oom oom'?
A cow walking
backwards.

What did the snake say when it was
offered a piece of cheese?
Thanks, I'll just have a slither.

What gets bigger the more you take away
from it?
A hole.

I went to the optician's to collect my
glasses and guess who I bumped into?
Everyone!

*What's the difference between a nail
and a boxer?*
One gets knocked in and one
gets knocked out.

> *Knock knock.*
> Who's there?
> *Scott.*
> Scott who?
> *Scott nothing to do with you.*

*Why did the Mexican throw his wife off the cliff?*
Tequila!

> *What did the rabbit say to the carrot?*
> It was nice gnawing you.

*What do you get when you cross a chicken with a cement mixer?*
A bricklayer.

*Waiter, Waiter, I can't eat this soup.*
*Call the manager.*
It's no use, Madam. He won't eat it either.

*Doctor, Doctor, I've broken my arm in two places.*
Well, don't go there again.

*My dog has no nose.*
Really, how does he smell?
*Terrible!*

*What kind of tree has hands?*
A palm tree.

*Why are hairdressers such good drivers?*
They know all the short cuts.

*What do you call a woman*
*with a sheep on her head?*
Baa-baa-ra.

*Why is a sofa like
a roast turkey?*
Because it's full
of stuffing.

*Why did the tuna go to Hollywood?*
She wanted to be a starfish.

*Why was the baby ant confused?*
Because all his uncles were ants.

*What has six legs but only uses four?*
A man on a horse.

*What's the tallest building?*
A library because it has so many stories.

*What do you call a pig with no clothes on?*
Streaky bacon.

*What happened when two fat men were in a race?*
One ran in short bursts and the other ran in burst shorts.

*Why did your brother wear a wet t-shirt all day?*
The label said wash and wear.

*What's white and yellow and travels*
*at 160 mph?*
A train driver's egg sandwich.

*Why do some people like eating snails?*
Because they don't like fast food.

PIANIST: Do you think I have
a gift for playing?
DAD: No, but I'll give you
a gift for stopping.

What do you call a man who forgets
to put his pants on?
Nicholas.

How do you know that carrots are
good for your eyesight?
Have you ever seen a rabbit
wearing glasses?

Did you hear about the man on
a seafood diet?
If he saw food, he ate it.

*Why is school like a shower?*
One wrong turn and you're in hot water.

*What begins with a P and ends with
an E and has a million letters in it?*
A Post Office.

*What kind of crisps can fly?*
Plane.

*What do you call a sleeping dinosaur?*
A dinosnore.

*Knock knock.*
Who's there?
*Justin.*
Justin who?
*Justin in time for school, ha ha.*

*What happens to a cat if it eats a lemon?*
It turns into a sourpuss.

*Why did Horrid Henry take an empty doughnut to the dentist?*
He wanted to get a filling.

*Why is the letter T like an island?*
Because it's in the middle of water.

*Why does a seagull live near the sea?*
If it lived near the bay, it'd be a bagel.

*What song did they play when the baker got married?*
Here crumbs the bride.

*What do you call a boy with a spade
on his head?*
Doug.

*What do you call a boy without a spade
on his head?*
Douglas.

*How do you make an octopus laugh?*
Ten tickles.

*Which bird succeeds?*
A budgie without any teeth.

*What's a pelican's favourite dish?*
Anything that fits the bill.

*What did the little bird say to the big bird?*
  Peck on someone your own size.

*What do you call a man who likes doing
exercise?*
Jim.

  *What's always coming, but never arrives?*
  Tomorrow.

*How did the baker get an electric shock?*
He stood on a bun and a current ran up
his leg.

*Who gets the
sack as soon as he
starts work?*
A postman.

*What goes, "Quick-quick!"?*
A duck with the hiccups.

*What do you call a clumsy bee?*
A tumble bee.

*Why did the
girl throw the
butter out of
the window?*
To see a
butter fly.

*Why couldn't the chicken find her eggs?*
She mislaid them.

*When's the best time
to buy a bird?*
When it's going
"cheep cheep".

*What happens if you call 666?*
You get an upside-down policeman.

*What do you call a man with
a paper bag on his head?*
Russell.

*Why did Singing Soraya climb the ladder?*
To reach the high notes.

*Why did the boy climb the ladder?*
He wanted to get to high school.

*Why is your pet always smiling?*
Because it's a grinny pig.

*What do you call a man with a truck on his head?*
Laurie.

*What's worse than an elephant with a sore trunk?*
A centipede with sore feet.

*Why can't you tell*
*Humpty Dumpty*
*a joke?*
Because he'll crack up.

*What did one wall say to the other wall?*
Meet you at the corner.

*Waiter, Waiter, what do you call this?*
It's bean soup, sir.
*I don't care what it's been –*
*what is it now?*

*Why did the chicken cross the road?*
To get to the shop.
*Did you find that funny? Well, neither did*
*the chicken because the shop was closed.*

*Why did the girl study on the aeroplane?*
She wanted a higher education

*Why couldn't the pirate play cards?*
Because he was standing on the deck.

*What do you call a piece of wood with nothing to do?*
Bored.

*Doctor, Doctor, I feel like a racehorse.*
Take one of these every four laps.

*Why did the banana go to the doctor?*
He wasn't peeling well.

*What do you call two robbers?*
A pair of knickers.

*What do you call an eight-legged cat?*
An octopussy.

*Why was the computer so cold?*
Because its windows were open.

*How did the bubblegum cross the road?*
It was stuck to the chicken's foot.

*What do you call a quiet bee?*
A mumble bee.

# EVEN MORE PURPLE JOKES

PETER: Henry, look, my tongue's gone purple.

HENRY: **Bleccch! Go and stick it out at Margaret.**

PETER: Will that help?

HENRY: **No, but I don't like Margaret.**

*What's purple and leaps from a tree?*
A squirrel.
*Why is it purple?*
Because it choked on a nut.

*What colour do you get when
you pull a burp?*
Burp-pull.

*What's purple and rides a horse?*
Alexander the Grape.

MARGARET: Knock Knock.
SUSAN: Who's there?
MARGARET: The purple.
SUSAN: The purple who?
MARGARET: The purple who
  live next door.

*What's purple with a hundred hairy legs?*
I don't know, but there's one running
up your leg.

*What's a cat's favourite colour?*
Purrrrrrr-ple.

*What's big, purple and ugly?*
You!

*What do you call a purple dinosaur
with a banana in each ear?*
Anything you like –
he can't hear you.

HORRID HENRY: **What rhymes with red?**

LAZY LINDA: Bed.

HORRID HENRY: **What rhymes with green?**

PERFECT PETER: Bean

HORRID HENRY: **What rhymes with blue?**

RUDE RALPH: **Boo!**

HORRID HENRY: **What rhymes with purple?**

BEEFY BERT: I dunno.

**Do you?**

**Horrid Henry** would like to thank all the Purple Hand Gang members who sent in their totally brilliant, utterly wicked jokes.

Mia, Leicester

George, London

Jordan, Scarborough

Olivia, Rotherham

Cristina, Liverpool

Matt, Eastleigh

Nadine, UK

Murtaza, Sharjah

Izzy, Wigan

Raahul, Harrow

Katie, Liverpool

Mileena, Ipswich

Kapitalina, Antwerp

Caitlin, Dunedin

Ollie, Perthshire
David, Glasgow
Alex, Scunthorpe
Jodie, UK
Lily, UK
Gemma, Birmingham
Megan, South Woodham
Bilal Ahmed, Halifax
Abigail, England
Shyla, India
Kayaiya, London
Max, Gatley
Aminath, UK
Saaraj, Preston
Lauren, Hampshire
Jack, Doncaster
Phillipa, Coventry
Mitchell, London
Rebekah, Shropshire
Charlotte, Birmingham
Maisie, Rugby
Lois, Preston

Imogine, Manchester
Shauna, Nottingham
Jasmin, Leeds
Farwah, Luton
Rohail, London
Cameron, Lincolnshire
Alysha, England
Ari, UK
Ellie, UK
Rahul, England
Chantel, Norwich
Calum, Manchester
Emma, New Milton
Dana, Barwell
Kirsten, Greystone
Kelly, London
Beth, Lancaster
Messy, London
Maria, England
Chazii, Cambridge
Faye, Enfield
Alex, Slough

Sally, Trowbridge

Sahar, London

Bethany, England

Rico, London

Shane-Deon, London

Rebecca, Truro

Lauren, Leeds

Rachel, St Helens

Megan, Romford

Jasmine, Shropshire

Megan, Manchester

Eleanor, Chorley

Ryan, Kincardine

Ben, Wigan

Holly, UK

Benjamin, Leicester

Sannah, Birmingham

Liam, London

Libby, Coventry

David, Flintshir

Tiegan, UK

Evie, Epsom

Alfie, Essex

Kerry, Coventry

Robbie, Sedbergh

Ben, Milverton

Hannah, Blackburn

Bethany, Matlock

Suneet, Dublin

Kimran, Birmingham

Amana, London

Kayleigh, Ireland

Bethany, London

Leah, Bradford

Jennifer, Northampton

Courtney, Andover

Jessica, Warrington

Ben, London

Megan, Bury

Louise,

   Stoke on Trent

Britney, UK

Emma, Liverpool

Francesca, Dubai

Rebekah, UK

Kirsten, Glasgow

Aimee, Leeds

Holly, Blackburn

Ellie, Liverpool

Yasmine, Cowley

Ellie, Yorkshire

Miriam, Gloucester

Jasmine, Aylesbury

Bradley, UK

Lucy, Oldham

Talha, Manchester

Orla, England

Bobbi, Liverpool

Shea, Armagh

Leah, Manchester

Chloe, UK

Emma, England

Ellie, Wirral

Ellie, Littleborough

Danielle, Basingstoke

Mia, London

Lauren, Liverpool

Dominic, Ellesmere Port

Everette, Baltimore

Madeline, Leeds

Caitlin, Dublin

Roshni, London

Craig, Bishops Stortford

Lucia, London

Libby, Bolton

Cara, Norwich

Luca, Brighton & Hove

Joe, Derby

Mia, Manchester

Alisha, Mexico City

Kaisha, England

Joshua, Swindon

Sammy, UK

Susiksha, England

Ben, Hull

Lucy, UK

Jasmin, Wolverhampton

Sam, Bradford

Ahsan, London

Jay, South Ockendon

Lewis, London

Holly, Chatham

Jack, London

Morgan, Scotland

Mark, Leicester

Tammy, Sheffield

Jade, Hastings

Leah, London

Ben, Taunton

Rebecca, Harrogate

Callum, Tividale

Yusuf, London

James, Lisbon

Zoe, Birmingham

Sarah, Nottingham

Jacob, Liverpool

Ellis, Malvern

Samuel, Ajman

Lauren, Dollingstown

Teesta, Mumbai

Zoya, Manchester

Maryam, London

Saheem, Northampton

Caitlin, Durham

Caleb, Chongqing

Jess, Swanwick

Marie, Hampshire

Mairi, Stirling

Grace, London

Lewis, Newcastle

Chelsea-May, Redditch

Emma, Cumbernauld

Neil, Dundalk

Jake, Bristol

Bob, New York

Katie, St Albans

Evie, Manchester

Mary, London

Charlie, Woking

Eve, Monmouthshire

Mariam, Birmingham

Tony, Glasgow
Daniel, London
Rachel, Jakarta
Kanisha, Bangalore
Harry, Stone
Katie, Wanstead
Julia, Oswestry
Tyler, Wakefield
Lilly, Paris
Hannah, Ipswich
Irandip, Wolverhampton
Henna, Oldham
Thomas, UK
Amal, Birmingham
Lillee, Plymouth
Haroon, Birmingham
Hassan, Dublin
Lucas, Guernsey
Ned, Purley
Teeba, London
Mhairi, Torphins
Paige, Newark

Erin, Barrhead
Lucia, Margate
Toby, Congleton
Alessio, London
Mia, Kent
Alice, Swadlincote
Anant, Mumbai
Kamilla, Stourport
Harrison, Manchester
Christopher, UK
Alex, Essex
Rebecca, Middlesbrough
Joel, Peterhead
Kirsty, Belfast
Elizabeth, London
Jasmine, Portsmouth
Lydia, Cleveland
Alice, England
Shannon, Tadworth
Nikita, Torrington
Joshua, Essex
Ashleigh, Oldham

Isabel, Exeter

Adam, Douglas

Pearse, Dublin

Jessica, Liverpool

Presley, Manchester

Brandon, Crewe

Dylan, Shrewsbury

Lucy, Chatham

Ellie, Mistley

Charlotte,
Farnham

Jake, Dublin

Shania, Solihull

Nathan, Preston

Rihanna, London

Sabbir, London

Shreyas, Milton Keynes

Emily, Dublin

Rhianna, Oxford

Jane, London

Emily, London

Joey, London

James, Leeds

Talia, Oldham

Alisha, Birmingham

Darcy, Durham

Hafsa, Manchester

Bláthnaid, Carrickmore

Vikram, Newcastle

Nina, UK

Megan, London

Hashim, London

Charlie, Bristol

Adam, London

Britney, Newcastle

Finn, Middlesbrough

Patrick, Belfast

Catherine, Liverpool

Louise, Pontypridd

Salom, Luton

Jake, Manchester

Kelsey, Retford

Niamh, Highwycombe

Gabriella, Durban

Lily, Cape Town

Georgia, Hull

Charlotte, London

Zaynab, Birmingham

Colm, Kerry

Antara, Kolkata

Thea, Chichester

Matthew, Walsall

Faith, Kent

Linards, Ireland

Liberty, Haringey

Kiera, Leamington

Aidan, Manchester

Ben, Sutton

Susanna, London

Conor, Dunbar

Luke, Cork

Ewan, UK

Sana, Al Ain

Georgia, Reigate

Louie, Reading

Sara, London

Clio, Newtown

Michelle, London

Abinaya, Stevenage

Josie, London

Lauren, UK

Callum, Paisley

Eli, Wales

Nicole, Dundrod

Teuta, Harrow

Jessica, Bedford

Afiq, Singapore

Tamsin, Thanet

Bobbie, Grimsby

Megan, Wolverhampton

Sharna, Westcliff

Tyler,

   Paddock Wood

Jodie, Shropshire

Shah, London

Gemma, Johannesburg

Brittany, Victoria

Shaye, London

Maya, Tipton

Sian, Plymouth

Holly, Lancaster

Dhruv, Chennai

Rosie, Coventry

Toby, Derby

Camila, London

Jessica, Eastbourne

Chloe, Kirkby

Liam, Carlisle

Jed, Newcastle

Esha, Rochdale

Alfie, Coventry

Yasmin, Manchester

Isabelle, Scotland

Jessica, Nottingham

Sophie, Saltash

Jolene, Belfast

Kyra, UK

Jack, Dagenham

Mohammed, Qatar

Hannah, Dunfermline

Aishwarya, Lusaka

Oliver, Croydon

Saz, New York

Anzum, London

Abi, Newcastle

GuanMin, Singapore

Jackie, London

Cassy, Liverpool

Zara, Birmingham

Katie, Oswestry

Samuel, Andover

Stephanie, Newbury

Olivia, UK

Gemma, Luton

Kieran, UK

Jada, London

Phil, Liverpool

Maxine, Surrey

Paul, Liverpool

Eleanor, Benfleet

Luke, Oldham

Nerissa, Eastbourne

Mayyah, Northampton

Tegan, UK

Evie, Leicestershire

Emily, Leipzig

Jude, Richmond

Harrison, Brereton

Monet, London

Sian, Tamworth

Adrienne, Northampton

Hannah, Newport

Sajeevan, London

Grace, West Midlands

Ella, Waltham Cross

Jaya, Orpington

Gemma, UK

Jade, Lydd

Liberty, Portsmouth

Megan, Wales

Emily, Bridgend

Moo, USA

Donna, England

Clio, Powys

Jasmine, Rugby

Michael, Lochgilphead

Alexia, Wimbledon

Leela, Broadstairs

Thomas, Tapei City

Rory, Shipley

Chloe, England

Samantha, Caterham

Kirstin, Watford

Shazna, Woking

Amy, Shrewsbury

Ceri, Forfar

Leilla, Surbiton

Owen, Harwich

Sophie, Nottinghamshire

Evie, Grimsby

Olivia, Plymouth

Jaya, West Yorkshire

Adil, Preston

Caitlin, Kilsyth

Nicole, Billericay

Lauren, England

Liberty, Nottingham    Millie, Rugby

Chantelle, York    Marie, Rushall

Shanaj, London    Josh, Basildon

Anya, Northampton    Lia, Blackpool

Max, London    Jonathan, Ipswich

Oliver, Sidcup    Zac, Brighton

Maebh, Co. Cork    Celie, London

Libby, Manchester    Georgia, England

Jodi, Glasgow    Ivan, East Kilbride

Millie, Guernsey    Jaz, Kent

Joshua, Walsall    Kelsey, London

Morgan, Glasgow    Claudia, Cirencester

Jadene, Helston    Reilly, Derbyshire

William, Tunbridge Wells    Kirandeep, Coventry

Deana, Newark    Elysia, UK

 Chloe,    Liam, Norwich

Nottingham    Aaqib, Bradford

Luke, Derby    Ellie, Darlington

Benjamin,    Katie, Roscommon

Studham    Lily, Rushden

Jake, Leeds    Sandhya, England

Stephen, Rushall    Kishan, London

Lauren, Dunstable

Lauren, Southend on Sea

Gemma, Falkirk

Courtney, Sunderland

Priya, Birmingham

Connor, Burntisland

Georgia, Marton

Yagoda, London

Tracey, Airdrie

Isaac, Nottingham

Megan, Whitely

Nasar, Burton

Tom, London

Abigail, Peterborough

Amber, Hartlepool

Annabelle, Wilmslow

Elliot, Taunton

Charley, Nottingham

Raeece, Manchester

Zain, Manchester

Keita, Preston

Georgia, Blackpool

Cariad, Essex

Zhanae, Nottingham

Myles, Manchester

Devon, Egham

Elana, Scotland

Mollie, Manchester

Ethan, Nottingham

Musab, Manchester

Ella, Swansea

Maryam, Didcot

Callum, Kirkcudbright

Kitty, Coventry

Rebecca, London

Finley, Lee on the Solent

India, Clevedon

Joe, Stoke

Bobbie-May, Kingstanding

Sam, Belfast

Ella, Leicestershire

Emily, Hockley

Toni, Lincoln

Susie, London     Megan, Spalding
Krishma, Staffs     Leanne, Glasgow
Farhan, London     Richard, Longford
Louise, Great Wyrley     Georgia, Sheffield
Madina, England     Ali, Harlow
Manoli, London     Zachary, Nantwich
Melvin, London     Jake,
Marsha, Ascot       Wolverhampton
Fenton, Hoghton     Morgan, Barnsley
Georgia, London     Jack, UK
Courtney, Liverpool     Evie, Willenhall
Clara, Chichester     Ryan, Manchester

# HORRID HENRY'S
# ALL TIME
# FAVOURITE
## JOKE BOOK

# CONTENTS

# HELLO
# FROM HENRY

Tee hee! Just when your parents and annoying brothers and sisters thought they'd heard all of your mega-watt killer jokes, my all time best joke book is here to save the day. These fantastically funny jokes will guarantee non-stop laughs. Why should you have to listen to boring story CDs in the car when everyone can listen to YOU instead? Purple Hand Gang - Henry's ultimate, deluxe, super-whopper mega joke book has arrived.

Keep laughing!                    Henry

# HORRID HENRY'S TOP TEN BONKERS BEASTS

*What do you get if you sit under a cow?*
A pat on the head.

*Why don't leopards cheat in exams?*
Because they know they'll be spotted.

*How does an elephant get down from a tree?*
He sits on a leaf and waits for it to fall.

*What's worse than an elephant with
a sore trunk?*
A centipede with sore feet.

*When is it bad luck to be followed
by a black cat?*
When you're a mouse.

*Why do giraffes have long necks?*
Because their feet smell.

*What's orange and sounds like a parrot?*
A carrot.

*When's the best time to buy a bird?*
When it's going "cheep cheep".

*What do you get when you cross*
*a sheep with a kangaroo?*
A woolly jumper.

*Waiter, waiter, do you serve fish?*
Sit down, sir, we serve anyone.

# DAFT DOCTORS

*Doctor, Doctor, I swallowed a dictionary.*
Don't breathe a word to anyone.

*Doctor, Doctor, I can't feel my legs!*
That's because I've cut off your arms.

*Doctor, Doctor, I think I'm a little overweight.*
Nonsense, pull up three chairs and we'll
talk about it.

*Doctor, Doctor, how can I stop feeling run-down?*
Try looking both ways before you cross the road.

*What do you call someone who sits in a doctor's waiting room for hours and hours?*
Patient.

*Where do ships go when they are ill?*
To the docks.

*Doctor, Doctor, I swallowed a bone.*
Are you choking?
*No, I really did.*

*Doctor, Doctor, how do I stop my nose from running?*
Stick your foot out and trip it up.

*Doctor, Doctor, I feel like a pack of cards.*
I'll deal with you later.

*Doctor, Doctor, my sister thinks she's a lift.*
Well, tell her to come and see me.
*She can't — she doesn't stop at this floor.*

*Doctor, Doctor, I snore so loudly*
*I keep myself awake.*
Sleep in another room then.

*Doctor, Doctor, when I press with my*
*finger here, it hurts — and when I press*
*here, it hurts — and here and here.*
*What's wrong with me?*
You've got a broken finger!

# COMPUTER CRACK-UPS

*Why did the computer go to the doctor's?*
It had a nasty virus.

*Why did the computer wear glasses?*
To improve its website.

*What do computers have to look after?*
Their pet mouse.

*Why did the boy eat his computer?*
Because it was an Apple.

*What did the computer do at the beach?*
It put on screensaver and surfed the net.

*You Tube, Twitter, and Facebook are making a joint website. What's it going to be called?*
You-Twit-Face.

*Why did the computer go to a shoe shop?*
Because it was rebooting.

*Why was the computer overweight?*
It was always taking megabytes.

*What do you call a computer superhero?*
A screen saver.

*How did the computer criminal get out of jail?*
He pressed the escape key.

*What do computers eat?*
Microchips.

*What do you get when you cross
a computer with an elephant?*
Lots of memory.

# BONKERS BIRTHDAYS

*What do you say to the toothless granny on her birthday?*
Many gappy returns.

**DAD:** Would you like a pocket calculator for your birthday?
**HORRID HENRY:** No, thanks. I already know how many pockets I've got.

*What do you sing to an alien who's just arrived on this planet?*
Happy Earth-day to You.

**HORRID HENRY:** I've got my eye on that big shiny bike for my birthday.
**DAD:** Well, you'd better keep your eye on it, because you'll never get your bottom on it.

**MUM:** Did you like the dictionary
I gave you for your birthday?
**PERFECT PETER:** Yes, I've been
trying to find the words to thank you.

**DAD:** I'm trying to buy a present for
my son. Can you help me out?
**SHOP ASSISTANT:** Certainly, sir.
Which way did you come in?

*What did the bald man say when he got a
comb for his birthday?*
Thanks, I'll never part with it.

*Knock knock.*
Who's there?
*Rabbit.*
Rabbit who?
*Rabbit up neatly. It's a birthday present.*

*What's the best birthday present in the world?*
A broken drum, you can't beat it!

*What's the best birthday present for a skeleton?*
A mobile bone.

*What do you give a gorilla for his birthday?*
I don't know, but let's hope he likes it!

# BLECCCCH! VALENTINE'S DAY

*What did the finger say to the thumb?*
People will say we're in glove.

*What did the bee say to the flower?*
Hi, honey!

*What did the girl octopus say to the boy octopus?*
I want to hold your hand, hand, hand,
hand, hand, hand, hand, hand.

*What do farmers give their wives on*
*Valentine's Day?*
Hogs and kisses.

*Why did the boy bat fall in love with the girl bat?*
Because she was fun to hang around with.

*Did you hear about the short-sighted hedgehog?*
She fell in love with a hairbrush.

*Why is lettuce the most romantic vegetable?*
Because it's all heart.

*What kind of flowers did Henry give
Margaret on Valentine's Day?*
Cauliflowers.

*Who is Dracula most likely to
fall in love with?*
The girl necks
door.

*Knock knock.*
Who's there?
*Olive.*
Olive who?
*Olive you.*

*Why did the acrobats get married?*
They were head over heels in love.

*Knock knock.*
Who's there?
*Howard.*
Howard who?
*Howard you like a big kiss.*

*What do you call a very small Valentine?*
A Valentiny.

*What did the girl volcano say to the boy volcano on Valentine's Day?*
I lava you.

225

# EASTER EGGSTRAVAGANZA

*What happens when you throw eggs
at a Dalek?*
It's eggs–terminated!

*Why did Greedy Graham laugh at his
fried egg?*
He thought it was a really funny yolk.

*Why did the chicken carry an umbrella?*
The weather was foul.

*What happened when the chicken ate a
big pile of sage, onion and breadcrumbs?*
It was stuffed.

*What happens when you take the yolk
out of an egg?*
It's all white.

*What did Mr and Mrs Chicken
call their baby?*
Egg.

*Why does E.T. like omelettes?*
Because he's an Eggs-tra Terrestrial.

*What does Father Christmas do at Easter?*
Nothing. He egg-nores the whole thing.

*Why shouldn't you tell a joke to an
Easter egg?*
It might crack up.

*What's a chicken's favourite TV programme?*
The feather forecast.

*Doctor, Doctor, I think I'm a chicken.*
How long has this been going on?
*Ever since I was an egg.*

*What do you get when you cross
a chicken with a thief?*
A peck-pocket.

*Why couldn't the chicken find her eggs?*
She mislaid them.

*How do you catch a rabbit?*
Hide behind a tree and make a noise
like a carrot.

# SPORTING SILLIES

*Why did the winning football team spin their trophy round and round?*
It was the Whirled Cup.

*When was the first tennis match in space played?*
A lawn time ago in a galaxy far away.

*What do you get if you cross martial arts with soccer?*
Kung fu-tball.

Whose job is it to carry the cricket players to each match?
The coach.

Why did the footballer play in his kitchen?
It was a home game.

What lights up a football stadium?
A football match.

Why did the footballer run out of salt and pepper?
It was the end of the seasoning.

*Why did the snooker player feel off colour?*
He wasn't getting enough greens.

*What's the angriest part of the goal?*
The crossbar.

*What does Kung-Fu Kate like to eat?*
Karate chops.

*What did the footballer say when he burped during a game?*
Sorry, it was a freak hic.

*Why was the football stadium so chilly?*
It was full of fans.

*Which type of gymnastics are sheep best at?*
The asymmetric baaaaas.

**LAZY LINDA:** I've just seen the
doctor and he says I can't play netball.
**MISS BATTLE-AXE:** Oh, he's seen
you play too, has he?

*Did you hear about the goalie with the
piggy bank?*
He was always saving.

*Why didn't the dog play badminton?*
Because he was a boxer.

*Why did the football pitch become a triangle?*
Somebody took a corner.

*Why should you leave Aerobic Al's
trainers well alone?*
They're not to be
sniffed at.

If you have a referee in football, a referee in
rugby and a referee in boxing, what do you
have in bowls?
Pudding.

Why was the octopus a good footballer?
Because of his ten-tackles.

# HOLIDAY HOWLERS

*What do you say to someone who's climbed
to the top of a mountain?*
Hi!

*What do double agents play when they
go on holiday?*
I spy.

*Where did Moody Margaret go on holiday this year?*
Alaska.
*Don't worry, I'll ask her myself.*

*Where do zombies go on holiday?*
The Deaditerranean.

*If I'm standing at the North Pole, facing the South Pole, and the east is on my left, what's on my right hand?*
Your fingers.

*Doctor, Doctor, I keep thinking I'm an alien.* Nonsense, you just need a holiday. *You're right – I've heard Mars is nice this time of year.*

**MISS BATTLE-AXE:** What did you learn during the summer holidays, Henry?
**HORRID HENRY:** That seven weeks isn't long enough to tidy my bedroom.

**DAD:** I hate to say this, but your swimming costume is very tight.
**MUM:** Wear your own then.

*Why did the clown throw cream pies at the audience?*
It was jest for fun.

**DAD:** Did you enjoy your trip to the seaside?
**HORRID HENRY:** No – a crab bit my toe!
**DAD:** Which one?
**HORRID HENRY:** I don't know – all crabs look the same to me.

**MAN:** I'd like a return ticket, please.
**CLERK:** Certainly, sir. Where to?
**MAN:** Back here, of course.

*How is the sea held in place?*
It's tied.

*Why did the monkey sunbathe?*
To get an orangu-tan.

# FUNNY FOOD

*How do you know a sausage doesn't like being fried?*
Because it spits!

*What do you get when you cross roast pork with a telephone?*
Crackling on the line.

*What stays hot, even in the fridge?*
Mustard.

*What does Horrid Henry call Perfect Peter*
*when he's stepped in syrup?*
Gooey-Two-Shoes.

*Why is a tomato round and red?*
Because if it was long and green it would
be a cucumber.

*What do you get when you cross a pig
with a centipede?*
Bacon and legs.

**CUSTOMER:** Get me something to eat
and make it snappy!
**WAITER:** How about a crocodile
sandwich?

*If you have five potatoes, how do you
share them between three people?*
Mash them.

*Where do you learn how
to make ice cream?*
Sundae school.

*Why did the banana peel?*
It forgot to put on any sun cream.

*Why did Greedy Graham eat his dinner
with a spade?*
He likes to shovel it down.

*Why do aliens have trouble drinking tea?*
Because of the flying saucers.

*Why was the banana afraid to snore?*
In case it woke up the rest of the bunch.

**AEROBIC AL:** I'm going swimming after my lunch.
**HORRID HENRY:** Really, I'm getting mine from the take-away.

# CLASSROOM CHAOS

A man escaped from prison by digging a tunnel under his cell. When he emerged, he was in the middle of a school playground. "I'm free!" cried the man. "So what?" said a little girl. "I'm four."

**HORRID HENRY:** Miss, my pen's run out.

**MISS BATTLE-AXE:** Well, go and chase after it then.

*Why are school chips like a history lesson?* Because you get to discover ancient grease.

**MISS BATTLE-AXE:** Give me a sentence using the word "fascinate".

**SOUR SUSAN:** My coat has ten buttons, but I can only fasten eight.

**MISS BATTLE-AXE:** Why have you painted black and white squares all over the computer screen?
**HORRID HENRY:** I wanted to check my emails.

*What's easy to get into at school, but hard to get out of?*
Trouble.

*Why was Horrid Henry's packed lunch so stinky?*
It had passed its smell-by-date.

**MISS BATTLE-AXE:** Where is Timbuktu?

**HORRID HENRY:** Between Timbuk-one and Timbuk-three.

**MISS BATTLE-AXE:** You're late again, Henry. What's your excuse this time?

**HORRID HENRY:** I ran here so fast, I didn't have time to think of one.

**BRAINY BRIAN:** Dad, Dad, I got an A in spelling.

**DAD:** Don't be silly, Brian! There's isn't an A in spelling.

*Why did Beefy Bert spread glue on his head?*
To help things stick in his mind.

**MISS BATTLE-AXE:** Give me a sentence using the word "benign".

**HORRID HENRY:** This year, I'll be eight – but next year I benign.

**MISS BATTLE-AXE:** Why are you crawling into school? And you're ten minutes late!

**HORRID HENRY:** Well, you said you didn't want to see me walking in late again.

**MISS BATTLE-AXE:** Can you name two birds that can't fly?

**HORRID HENRY:** An ostrich and a dead parrot.

**HORRID HENRY:** I'm phoning to say I won't be able to come to school today.
**MISS BATTLE-AXE:** Why not?
**HORRID HENRY:** I've lost my voice.

*Which word of five letters has six left when you take two away?*
Sixty.

**MISS BATTLE-AXE:** If I cut three apples, four oranges and two pears into ten pieces each, what will I have?
**GREEDY GRAHAM:** A fruit salad.

**TOUGH TOBY:** I want to be a rubbish collector when I grow up.
**MISS BATTLE-AXE:** But you haven't got any experience.
**TOUGH TOBY:** I'll just pick it up as I go along.

# MEGA MONEY

*Why did Henry put his money in the freezer?*
He wanted cold, hard cash.

*How much did the pirate's earrings cost?*
A buccaneer.

*What's the quickest way to double your money?*
Fold it in half.

*What do you get if you cross a sorceress with a millionaire?*

*Why is money called dough?*
Because we all knead it.

**HORRID HENRY:** What would you do if a bull charged you?
**ANXIOUS ANDREW:** I'd pay whatever it charged.

*What happened when Fluffy swallowed a pound?*
There was money in the kitty.

**MR MOSSY:** You're very quiet today, Henry.

**HORRID HENRY:** Well, Mum gave me a pound not to say anything about your red nose.

*Why did Robin Hood steal money from the rich?* Because the poor didn't have any.

# DAFT DINOSAURS

*What do you do with a green dinosaur?*
Wait till it ripens.

*What do dinosaurs put on their chips?*
Tomatosaurus.

*What does a Triceratops sit on?*
Its Tricera-bottom.

*What do you get when you cross a dinosaur with a lemon?*
A dino-sour.

*What do you call a dinosaur that left its armour out in the rain?*
A stegosaurust.

*What do you call a dinosaur that never gives up?*
A try-try-try-ceratops.

*What do you call a dinosaur wearing high heels?*
My-feet-are-saurus.

*What do you call a dinosaur who is always
walking in the mud?*
Brown-toe-saurus.

*When can three giant dinosaurs hide under an
umbrella and not get wet?*
When it's not raining.

*Why do people avoid dinosaurs?*
Because their eggs stink.

# MONSTER MANIA

*What does the polite monster say when he meets people for the first time?*
Pleased to eat you.

*Why was the monster called Fog?*
Because he was thick and grey.

*How do you greet a three-headed monster?*
Hello, hello, hello.

*Why did the monster cross the road?*
To eat the chicken.

*The police are looking for a monster with one eye.*
Why don't they use two?

*What did the monster eat at Restaurant Le Posh?*
The waiter.

*What do you call an alien with three eyes?*
Aliiien.

*How do monsters cook their food?*
They terror-fry it.

*What is an ogre's favourite flavour squash?*
Lemon and slime.

*What do monsters like best for pudding?*
Eyes-cream.

*What do you call a monster with no neck?*
The Lost Neck Monster.

What time was it when the monster
swallowed the Prime Minister?
Ate P.M.

What do you call a monster with a big hairy
nose, pointed yellow teeth and red eyes?
Ugly.

What do you call a monster with a big
hairy nose, pointed yellow teeth, red eyes
and no legs?
Still ugly.

# ANIMAL MADNESS

*What goes "stomp, stomp, stomp, squelch"?*
An elephant wearing wet trainers.

*What do you get if you cross a chicken with a guitar?*
A hen that makes music when you pluck it.

*Two elephants walked off a cliff ...*

Boom! Boom!

*Why don't you see penguins in Great
Britain?*
Because they're afraid of Wales.

*Have you got any dogs going cheap?*
No, all mine go "Woof".

A man took his dog to the vet, and said, "My dog is cross-eyed – is there anything you can do?"
The vet picked up the dog and carefully examined him. Finally, he said, "I'm going to have to put him down."
"Why?" said the man. "Just because he's cross-eyed?"
"No," said the vet. "Because he's very heavy."

*What do you get when you cross a monkey with a flower?*
A chimp-pansy.

*What do you call one bee with another bee
on its back?*
A double-decker buzz.

*What do you get when you cross a cow
with a duck?*
Cream quackers.

*What do you get when you cross a parrot
with a shark?*
An animal that talks your head off.

*Where would you find a dog with no legs?*
Exactly where you left it.

*Which is richer? A cow or a bull?*
A bull – because the cow gives you
milk, but the bull charges.

*What kind of cheese would you use to disguise
a horse?*
Mascarpone.

*What kind of dog is always in a hurry?*
A dash-hound.

*Why was the bee's hair sticky?*
Because he used a honey-comb.

*What did the goose get when he was cold?*
People-pimples.

*What do you get when you cross a mouse with an orange?*
A pipsqueak.

*What's the difference between a well-dressed man and a tired dog?*
The man wears a suit – the dog just pants.

# HALLOWE'EN HOOTS

*What happens when a ghost gets a fright?*
He jumps into his skin.

*What's the scariest squidgiest day of the year?*
Marshmallowe'en.

*What's a vampire's favourite kind of ice cream?*
Vein-illa.

*What did one ghost say to the other ghost?*
"Do you believe in people?"

*What do you call a vampire who likes to relax
in a bloodbath with a good book?*
Well red.

*What do you do when fifty zombies
surround your house?*
Hope it's Hallowe'en.

*Why didn't the witch wear a flat cap?*
There was no point.

*What is as sharp as a vampire's fang?*
His other fang.

*How do you join the Dracula fan club?*
Send your name, address and blood group.

*What kind of jewellery do witches wear?*
Charm bracelets.

*Do zombies eat crisps with their fingers?*
No, they eat the fingers separately.

*What happens when a ghost*
*gets lost in the fog?*
He is mist.

*What kind of make-up do witches wear?*
Mas-scare-a.

*What's the difference between a deer
running away and a small witch?*
One's a hunted stag, the other's
a stunted hag.

# CRAZY CREEPY-CRAWLIES

**SLUG:** Who's that sitting on your back?
**SNAIL:** That's Michelle.

*How deep is the water in a pond full of frogs?*
Knee-deep, knee-deep, knee-deep.

*How do you know which end of a worm is its head?*
Tickle it and see which end smiles.

*What does a toad say when he sees something he likes?*
"That's toad-ally awesome!"

*Why don't baby birds ever smile?*
Because their mothers feed them worms all day.

*Where do you find giant snails?*
On the end of a giant's fingers.

*How do frogs do DIY?*
With toad's tools.

*What is a tadpole after it is five days old?*
Six days old.

*What lies on the ground, a hundred feet in the air?*
A centipede.

# REALLY RUDE

*Why couldn't the knickers do any magical tricks?*
They were just pants.

*Knock knock.*
Who's there?
*Henrietta.*
Henrietta who?
*Henrietta bogey!*

*What's got a bottom at the top?*
A toilet.

*Did you hear about the grandfather clock
that was filled with mouldy cheese?*
It ponged every hour.

*What do you get if you cross ten aliens with Humpty Dumpty?*
Ten green bottoms hanging on a wall.

*What happened to the thief who stole a lorry load of knicker elastic?*
He was sent to prison for a long stretch.

*Which queen burped a lot?*
Queen Hic-toria.

*Which king had a noisy bottom?*
Richard the Lionfart.

*Knock knock.*
Who's there?
*Nicholas.*
Nicholas who?
*Nicholas girls shouldn't climb trees.*

*What's brown and sounds like a bell?*
Dung.

*What's the rudest vegetable?*
A pea.

*What's hairy,*
*scary and*
*wears knickers*
*on its head?*
The Under-werewolf.

*Who shouted knickers at the big bad wolf?*
Little Rude Riding Hood.

*Why do gorillas have big nostrils?*
Because they have big fingers.

# MOODY MOANERS

*What do you call a sad spaceship?*
An unidentified crying object.

*Have you ever seen a fish cry?*
No, but I've seen a whale blubber.

*What happened when Fluffy the cat ate
a lemon?*
She became a sourpuss.

*What's Moody Margaret's favourite day of the week?*
Moanday.

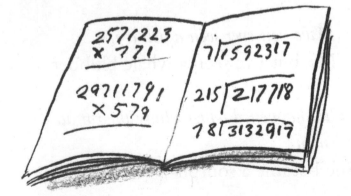

| M | T | W | T | F | S | S |
|---|---|---|---|---|---|---|
|   | 1 | 2 | 3 | 4 | 5 | 6 |
| 7 | 8 | 9 | 10 | 11 | 12 | 13 |
| 14 | 15 | 16 | 17 | 18 | 19 | 20 |
| 21 | 22 | 23 | 24 | 25 | 26 | 27 |
| 28 | 29 | 30 | 31 |   |   |   |

*Why was the maths book in a bad mood?*
It had a lot of problems.

*Why are adults always complaining?*
Because they are groan-ups.

*Which painting is always grumpy?*
The Moaning Lisa.

*Why did the cow have sour milk?*
Because she was mooooody.

# CHRISTMAS CRACKERS

*What do you call a reindeer who won't say please and thank you?*
Rude-olph.

*Where did the mistletoe go to become rich and famous?*
Hollywood.

*What bird has wings but can't fly?*
A roast turkey.

*What do snowmen sing at parties?*
Freeze a jolly good fellow?

*What jumps from cake to cake and tastes*
*of almonds?*
Tarzipan.

*Where do ghosts go for a Christmas treat?*
The phantomime.

*Have you heard the story of the three reindeer?*
No, I haven't.
*Oh dear, dear, dear.*

*What kind of bread do elves use to make sandwiches?*
Shortbread.

**ELF:** Santa, the reindeer swallowed my pencil. What should I do?
**SANTA:** Use a pen.

*Where is the best place to put your Christmas tree?*
Between your Christmas two and your Christmas four.

# HORRID HENRY BOOKS

## Storybooks

Horrid Henry

Horrid Henry and the Secret Club

Horrid Henry Tricks the Tooth Fairy

Horrid Henry's Nits

Horrid Henry Gets Rich Quick

Horrid Henry's Haunted House

Horrid Henry and the
Mummy's Curse

Horrid Henry's Revenge

Horrid Henry and the Bogey
Babysitter

Horrid Henry's Stinkbomb

Horrid Henry's Underpants

Horrid Henry Meets the Queen

Horrid Henry and the Mega-Mean
Time Machine

Horrid Henry and the Football Fiend

Horrid Henry's Christmas Cracker

Horrid Henry and the
Abominable Snowman

Horrid Henry Robs the Bank

Horrid Henry Wakes the Dead

Horrid Henry Rocks

Horrid Henry and the
Zombie Vampire

Horrid Henry's Monster Movie

Horrid Henry's Nightmare

Horrid Henry's Guide to
Perfect Parents

Horrid Henry's Krazy Ketchup

Horrid Henry's Cannibal Curse

## Early Readers

Don't Be Horrid Henry!

Horrid Henry's Birthday Party

Horrid Henry's Holiday

Horrid Henry's Underpants

Horrid Henry Gets Rich Quick

Horrid Henry and the Football Fiend

Horrid Henry Nits

Horrid Henry and Moody Margaret

Horrid Henry's Thank You Letter

Horrid Henry's Car Journey

Moody Margaret's School

Horrid Henry's Tricks and Treats

Horrid Henry's Rainy Day

Horrid Henry's Author Visit

Horrid Henry Meets the Queen

Horrid Henry's Sports Day

Moody Margaret Casts a Spell

Horrid Henry's Christmas Presents

Moody Margaret's Makeover

Horrid Henry and the Demon
Dinner Lady

Horrid Henry Tricks the Tooth Fairy

Horrid Henry's Homework

Horrid Henry and the Bogey
Babysitter

Horrid Henry's Sleepover

Horrid Henry's Wedding

Horrid Henry's Haunted House

Horrid Henry's Christmas Lunch

Horrid Henry's Mothers Day

Horrid Henry's Comfy Black Chair

Horrid Henry and the Mummy's Curse

## Colour Books

*Horrid Henry's Big Bad Book*
*Horrid Henry's Wicked Ways*
*Horrid Henry's Evil Enemies*
*Horrid Henry Rules the World*
*Horrid Henry's House of Horrors*
*Horrid Henry's Dreadful Deeds*
*Horrid Henry Shows Who's Boss*
*Horrid Henry's A-Z of
Everything Horrid*
*Horrid Henry Fearsome Four*
*Horrid Henry's Royal Riot*
*Horrid Henry's Tricky Tricks*

## Activity Books

*Horrid Henry's Brainbusters*
*Horrid Henry's Headscratchers*
*Horrid Henry's Mindbenders*
*Horrid Henry's Colouring Book*
*Horrid Henry's Puzzle Book*
*Horrid Henry's Sticker Book*
*Horrid Henry's Classroom Chaos*
*Horrid Henry's Holiday Havoc*
*Horrid Henry's Runs Riot*
*Horrid Henry's Annual 2015*
*Horrid Henry's Crazy Crosswords*
*Horrid Henry's Mad Mazes*
*Horrid Henry's Wicked Wordsearches*

## Joke Books

*Horrid Henry's Joke Book*
*Horrid Henry's Jolly Joke Book*
*Horrid Henry's Mighty Joke Book*
*Horrid Henry versus
Moody Margaret*
*Horrid Henry's Hilariously
Horrid Joke Book*
*Horrid Henry's Purple Hand Gang
Joke Book*
*Horrid Henry's All Time
Favourite Joke Book*

## Fact Books

*Horrid Henry's Ghosts*
*Horrid Henry's Dinosaurs*
*Horrid Henry's Sports*
*Horrid Henry's Food*
*Horrid Henry's Kings and Queens*
*Horrid Henry's Bugs*
*Horrid Henry's Animals*
*Horrid Henry's Ghosts*
*Horrid Henry's Crazy Creatures*
*Horrid Henry's World Records*

Visit **Horrid Henry's** website at www.horridhenry.co.uk
for competitions, games, downloads and a
monthly newsletter!